Snakehead

Star Pilot

Super Bug

Super Gloo

Princess Mighty

Super Lady   Jaws

Super Thor   Super caveman

Blade Warrior   # Celtic Warrior

Super Mum   # Jungle Man

Robin Hood   Dragon Queen

Sir-Lance-A-Lot

Hannibal

Super Duck

Hammer Head

Super Moose

Volgan

Buffalo Bill

Galactica

Super oil

Rope Breaker

The Bat

Globe Man

Space Robot

Space Baroness

Space Warrior   Sonic Hero

Mechanic Man

Demon Fighter

Demon Slayer   # Lightning Diver

UDDz

Captain Galactic

Ninja

Axeman

The Archer

Lightning

Sky Boxer

Venus Amazon

Star Warden

Spartacus

Star Hunter   Space Shield

Kajo

Zulu

Robot Warrior

Frogman

Space Sniper

Prince Sword

Karate King

Sky Diver

Super Saver

Samurai

Queen Boudicca

Aztec

Super Star

Sky Leaper

Swash Buccaneer

Space Skater

Lizardus

Surf Boarder

Super Egor

Skater

Space Queen

Super Charger

G.I.

Markovian Lancer

Greek Hero

Sky Scraper

Robo

Kango Kicker

Star Chaser

Rocky Hunter

Super Power

Android

Super Silly-us

Kongo

Star Skater

Arachnia

Layzar

Super Swooper

Super Nan

Barbarus

Super Flyer

Space Lancer

Super Spy

Goliath

Sitting Bull

Super Strongman

Space Saver

Iron Man

Super Boy

Super Woof

Super Bunny

Big Beard

Mighty Mog